A Father's Journal

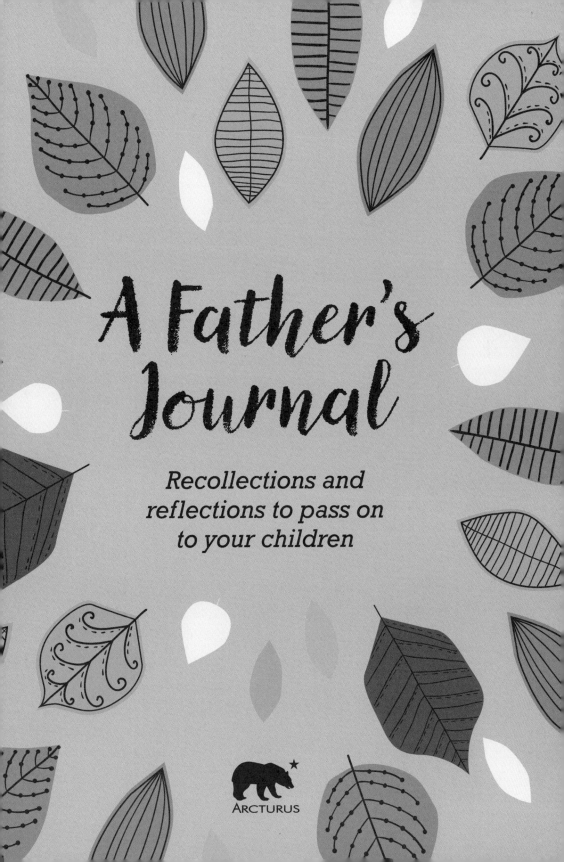

A Father's Journal

Recollections and reflections to pass on to your children

ARCTURUS

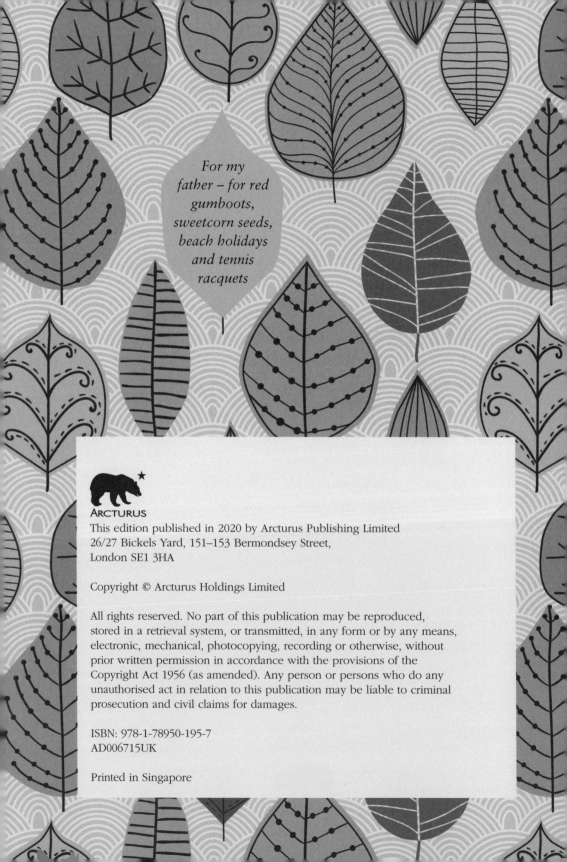

*For my
father – for red
gumboots,
sweetcorn seeds,
beach holidays
and tennis
racquets*

ARCTURUS

This edition published in 2020 by Arcturus Publishing Limited
26/27 Bickels Yard, 151–153 Bermondsey Street,
London SE1 3HA

ISBN: 978-1-78950-195-7
AD006715UK

Printed in Singapore

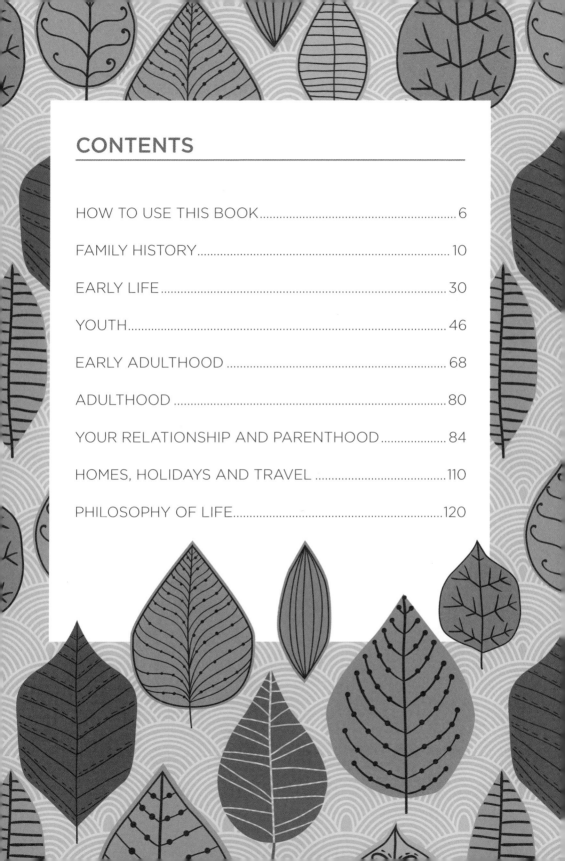

CONTENTS

HOW TO USE THIS BOOK.. 6

FAMILY HISTORY.. 10

EARLY LIFE.. 30

YOUTH... 46

EARLY ADULTHOOD 68

ADULTHOOD 80

YOUR RELATIONSHIP AND PARENTHOOD.................... 84

HOMES, HOLIDAYS AND TRAVEL 110

PHILOSOPHY OF LIFE...120

HOW TO USE THIS BOOK

If you don't ask, you'll never know.

Many of us are close to our fathers, maybe even talking to them every day or every week on the phone, regularly uploading photos for them to view via social media, or visiting them on Sundays for lunch or dinner. But during these brief moments of connection, so often our conversations relate to the 'here-and-now' and the immediate practicalities of day-to-day living: 'How are you feeling?', 'How did your appointment go?', 'How's the weather?', or 'What are you planning to do next week?' Others of us may be less close to our fathers, or may be separated by great distances, but nevertheless we are all connected by the same parent–child bond.

Sometimes, within a perfectly ordinary conversation a small comment might be made that suddenly makes us sit up and think, 'I never knew that!' and leads us to ask further questions. We often discover that the *right questions* can unlock reservoirs of memories that we never knew existed – and we soon realize that a whole lifetime of experiences and stories is there to be discovered, shared and talked about.

If only we had the time... if only we asked the right questions...

That's where *A Father's Journal* comes in. The idea behind this book is that you give it to your father as a gift and ask him to fill in the answers, or you complete it together creating precious new memories. It provides a structured framework for you and your father to delve into his past, unlocking memories of his parents (your grandparents), his childhood and school days, how he felt about becoming a father, and recording prized memories for you to read. It also includes questions about your father's hopes and dreams, how external events shaped the decisions he made, and the important life lessons he learned along the way.

The book takes the form of roughly chronological questions with spaces for you and your father to write in his answers. From simple questions about where your father grew up to the most significant, defining moments of his life – and especially insights and perspectives that he'd like to pass down to you – the narrative that unfolds is ultimately the story of who you are and where you've come from.

We've now commemorated the centenary of the end of World War I, and there's a rising consciousness and enthusiasm to record the memories and experiences of other generations before it's too late. All around us there are reminders that time is passing only too quickly, and with today's fast-paced life it is more important than ever to make time for our families. The sad reality is that we all have a limited time on Earth, and once our irreplaceable fathers are gone, their voices are gone too. It is never too soon to record these recollections which will be treasured by many generations to come.

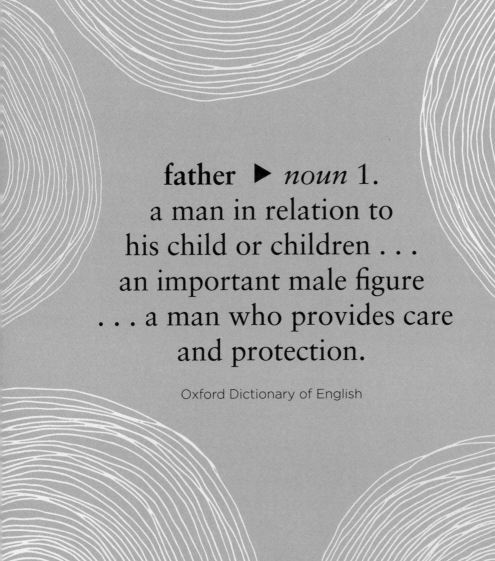

father ▶ *noun* 1.
a man in relation to
his child or children . . .
an important male figure
. . . a man who provides care
and protection.

Oxford Dictionary of English

What age are you now as you fill in this journal?

....

....

....

....

....

....

....

....

....

....

Where are you living?

....

....

....

....

....

....

....

....

....

....

....

....

....

List the full names, ages, dates of birth and addresses of your child or children.

....
....
....
....
....
....
....
....
....
....
....
....
....
....
....
....
....
....
....
....

FAMILY HISTORY

What is your father's name and date of birth?
Where was he born?

....

....

....

....

....

....

What is your mother's name and date of birth?
Where was she born?

....

....

....

....

....

....

Do you have any siblings? If so, what are their names and
dates of birth, and where were they born?

....

....

....

....

....

Draw your family tree. To help you get started, an example is shown here. Write in pencil first, then make each entry permanent once you're sure that the names and dates are correct.

Plot the youngest generation at the bottom of the page. Each box should contain the name of the person and their dates of birth, marriage and death ('b' for birth, 'm' for marriage and 'd' for death). Add vertical lines to connect each sibling to their parents. Females should be recorded with their maiden names. Use the '=' sign between boxes to indicate a marriage.

First draw your father's family tree overleaf, then your mother's.

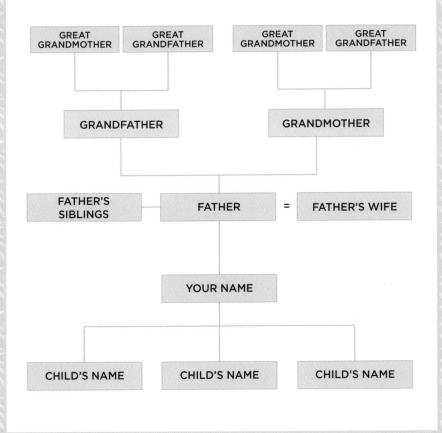

Draw your father's family tree.

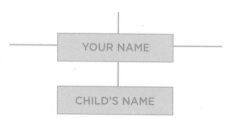

YOUR NAME

CHILD'S NAME

Draw your mother's family tree.

YOUR NAME

CHILD'S NAME

Where did your father grow up?

....

....

....

....

....

....

....

....

....

....

Did your father have brothers and sisters?
If so, what are their names?

....

....

....

....

....

....

....

....

....

What do you know about your father's childhood?

....

....

....

....

....

....

....

....

....

....

....

....

....

....

....

....

....

....

....

....

....

....

....

....

What do you know about your father's ancestry?

....
....
....
....
....
....
....
....
....
....
....
....
....
....
....
....
....
....
....
....
....

Where did your mother grow up?

....

....

....

....

....

....

....

....

....

....

Did your mother have brothers and sisters?
If so, what are their names?

....

....

....

....

....

....

....

....

....

What do you know about your mother's childhood?

....
....
....
....
....
....
....
....
....
....
....
....
....
....
....
....
....
....
....
....
....
....

What do you know about your mother's ancestry?

....
....
....
....
....
....
....
....
....
....
....
....
....
....
....
....
....
....
....
....
....

Where did your father go to school?

....

....

....

....

....

....

....

....

....

What were his hobbies?

....

....

....

....

....

....

....

....

....

Where did your mother go to school?

....
....
....
....
....
....
....
....
....

What were her hobbies?

....
....
....
....
....
....
....
....
....
....
....

Did your parents work? If so, what jobs did they do?

....
....
....
....
....
....
....
....
....
....
....
....
....
....
....
....
....
....
....
....
....
....

Did your parents get married? If so, when and where?

How old was your father when you were born?

....
....
....
....
....
....
....
....
....
....

How old was your mother when you were born?

....
....
....
....
....
....
....
....
....
....

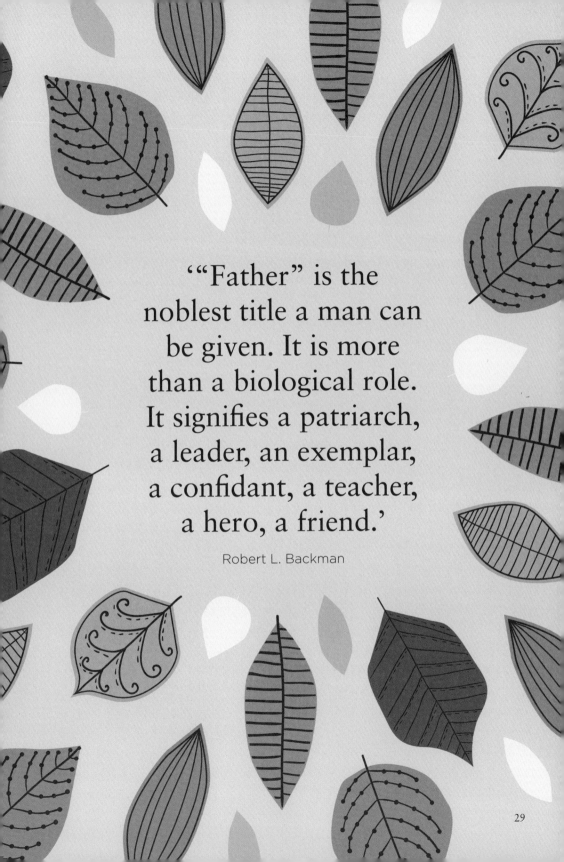

'"Father" is the noblest title a man can be given. It is more than a biological role. It signifies a patriarch, a leader, an exemplar, a confidant, a teacher, a hero, a friend.'

Robert L. Backman

EARLY LIFE

What was the date of your birth?

....

....

....

Which city or town were you born in?

....

....

....

....

....

....

....

Were you born at home or in a hospital?

....

....

....

....

....

....

....

....

What events were happening in the world around the time you were born?

....
....
....
....
....
....
....
....
....
....
....
....
....
....
....
....
....
....
....
....
....
....
....
....

What was your first address?

....

....

....

....

....

....

....

....

....

....

What do you remember about your first home?

....

....

....

....

....

....

....

....

....

....

....

....

What is your first memory?

....
....
....
....
....
....
....
....
....
....
....
....
....
....
....
....
....
....
....
....
....
....
....

What were your parents like? What was their parenting style?

....
....
....
....
....
....
....
....
....
....
....
....
....
....
....
....
....
....
....
....
....
....

What was your relationship with your parents like? Were you close to them?

What are your most precious memories of your father?

....
....
....
....
....
....
....
....
....
....

What are your most precious memories of your mother?

....
....
....
....
....
....
....
....
....
....
....

Did you see your grandparents often? What are your
fondest memories of them?

....

....

....

....

....

....

....

....

....

Who do you think you take after the most, and why?

....

....

....

....

....

....

....

....

....

....

....

What toys did you play with? Did you have a favourite?

....

....

....

....

....

....

....

....

....

....

....

....

....

....

....

....

....

....

....

....

....

What were your favourite games?

....
....
....
....
....
....
....
....
....
....

Did you have any pets? If so, what kind, and what were their names?

....
....
....
....
....
....
....
....
....
....

Did you go to pre-school or kindergarten?

....

....

....

....

....

....

What are your memories of that time?

....

....

....

....

....

....

....

....

....

....

....

....

....

....

....

What sort of child were you? Describe your personality when you were small.

....
....
....
....
....
....
....
....
....
....
....
....
....
....
....
....
....
....
....
....
....
....

What songs, stories or nursery rhymes did you like best when you were very young?

....
....
....
....
....
....
....
....
....
....

Did your parents play music in your home? What sort?

....
....
....
....
....
....
....
....
....
....

'Every father should remember one day his son will follow his example, not his advice.'

Charles Kettering

If you have any photographs of your parents, grandparents or you when you were very young, stick them in here.

YOUTH

Where and when did you go to school? Describe the building, your teachers and any other memories of school.

....

....

....

....

....

....

....

....

....

....

....

....

....

....

....

....

....

....

....

....

....

What were your favourite subjects at school?

....
....
....
....
....
....
....
....
....
....

What subjects did you dislike?

....
....
....
....
....
....
....
....
....
....
....

Did you play any sports? Which ones?

....
....
....
....
....
....
....
....
....
....

What were you best at, and why?

....
....
....
....
....
....
....
....
....
....
....

'My father didn't tell me how to live. He lived and let me watch him do it.'

Clarence Budington Kelland

What were your after-school hobbies?

Did you have any part-time jobs? What were they?

....
....
....
....
....
....
....
....
....
....
....
....
....
....
....
....
....
....
....
....
....
....
....

Describe your relationship with your siblings (if applicable).
Stick in some photographs of them.

....
....
....
....
....
....
....
....
....
....
....
....
....
....
....
....
....
....
....
....
....
....
....
....

What were your friends' names, and what were they like?

....

....

....

....

....

....

....

....

....

....

Where did you and your friends spend your time and what
did you do together?

....

....

....

....

....

....

....

....

....

....

Did you have a school uniform? If so, what was it like?

....
....
....
....
....
....
....
....
....
....

What clothes did you wear when you weren't at school?

....
....
....
....
....
....
....
....
....
....

What books or plays did you read or study at school?

....
....
....
....
....
....
....
....
....
....

What was your favourite book or play, and why?

....
....
....
....
....
....
....
....
....
....
....
....

What films did you see and what television shows did you watch?

....
....
....
....
....
....
....
....
....

What was your favourite film and/or television show, and why?

....
....
....
....
....
....
....
....
....
....
....
....

What kind of music did you listen to?

....

....

....

....

....

....

....

....

....

....

What was your favourite song or piece of music, and why?

....

....

....

....

....

....

....

....

....

....

....

....

How would your teachers have described you while you were at school?

....

....

....

....

....

....

What sort of grades did you get?

....

....

....

....

....

....

....

....

Were you popular? Were you ever a prefect or captain?

....

....

....

....

....

....

What sorts of meals did you eat? Describe your typical breakfast, lunch and dinner.

....
....
....
....
....
....
....
....
....
....
....
....
....
....
....
....
....
....
....
....
....
....

What was your favourite food, and what didn't you like?

....

....

....

....

....

....

....

....

....

....

Did you learn to cook? If so, what did you make?

....

....

....

....

....

....

....

....

....

....

....

What were your hopes and dreams when you were young?

....

....

....

....

....

....

....

....

....

....

....

....

....

....

....

....

....

....

....

....

....

....

....

What are the saddest memories from your childhood?

....

....

....

....

....

....

....

....

....

....

....

....

....

....

....

....

....

....

....

....

....

....

....

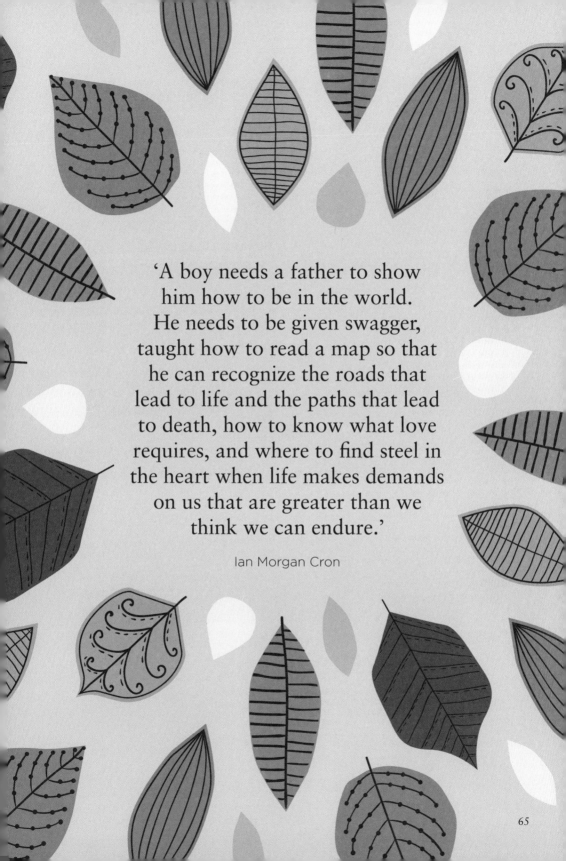

'A boy needs a father to show him how to be in the world. He needs to be given swagger, taught how to read a map so that he can recognize the roads that lead to life and the paths that lead to death, how to know what love requires, and where to find steel in the heart when life makes demands on us that are greater than we think we can endure.'

Ian Morgan Cron

Use this space to stick in photographs of you as a teenager.

EARLY ADULTHOOD

What was your parents' attitude towards education?

....

....

....

....

....

....

....

....

Did you do what your parents wanted you to, or something else? If so, what?

....

....

....

....

....

....

....

....

....

....

....

....

When did you leave school?

....

....

....

....

....

....

....

....

Did you get any qualifications?

....

....

....

....

....

....

....

....

....

....

....

....

What was happening in the world during your early adulthood? List the major events that you remember best.

....

....

....

....

....

....

....

....

....

How did external events influence your decisions about what you wanted to do?

....

....

....

....

....

....

....

....

....

....

....

....

'Fathers, you are your
daughter's hero. My father
was my hero. I used to wait
on the steps of our home for
him to arrive each night. He
would pick me up and twirl me
around and let me put my feet
on top of his big shoes, and
then he would dance me into
the house. I loved the challenge
of trying to follow his every
footstep. I still do.'

Elaine S. Dalton

When you were growing up, who were your role models?
Who inspired you the most, and why?

....

....

....

....

....

....

....

....

....

....

....

....

....

....

....

....

....

....

....

....

....

....

Where did you live when you first left home, and how old were you?

....

....

....

....

....

....

....

....

....

Did you miss home?

....

....

....

....

....

....

....

....

....

....

....

Did you go to university? Or did you go straight into a job?

....
....
....
....
....
....
....
....
....
....

Tell me about this time in your life.

....
....
....
....
....
....
....
....
....
....
....
....

Who were your closest friends, what were they like and what did they do?

....

....

....

....

....

....

....

....

....

Did you learn to drive? If so, when did you get your first car?

....

....

....

....

....

....

....

....

....

....

Who was your first crush?

....
....
....
....
....
....
....
....
....
....

When was your first kiss?

....
....
....
....
....
....
....
....
....
....
....
....

Did you date when you were younger?
If so, did you have any serious relationships?

....

....

....

....

....

....

Where did you go when you went on a date?

....

....

....

....

....

....

....

What was your hardest breakup like?

....

....

....

....

....

....

Did you go to parties or nightclubs?

....

....

....

....

....

....

....

....

....

What type of clothes were in fashion at the time, and what type of music was playing?

....

....

....

....

....

....

....

....

....

....

ADULTHOOD

What was your first real job? Can you remember how much you got paid?

....

....

....

....

....

....

....

What did you like best about your work?

....

....

....

....

....

....

....

What didn't you like?

....

....

....

....

....

Did you have a clear career path in mind, or did you try out different jobs?

....
....
....
....
....
....
....
....
....
....
....
....
....
....
....
....
....
....
....
....
....
....
....
....

List the main jobs you have had.

....

....

....

....

....

....

....

....

....

....

What were the highlights?

....

....

....

....

....

....

....

....

....

....

....

Write your signature below. Did it always look like this?

....

....

....

Draw some doodles or pictures in your own style.

YOUR RELATIONSHIP AND PARENTHOOD

Tell me about your most significant long-term relationship.

....

....

....

....

....

....

....

....

....

....

....

....

....

....

....

....

....

....

....

What events were happening in the world around the time
this relationship began?

....

....

....

....

....

....

....

....

....

....

....

....

....

....

....

....

....

....

....

....

Did you ever marry?

....

....

....

....

....

....

....

....

....

....

If not, did you do anything else to celebrate your
relationship?

....

....

....

....

....

....

....

....

....

....

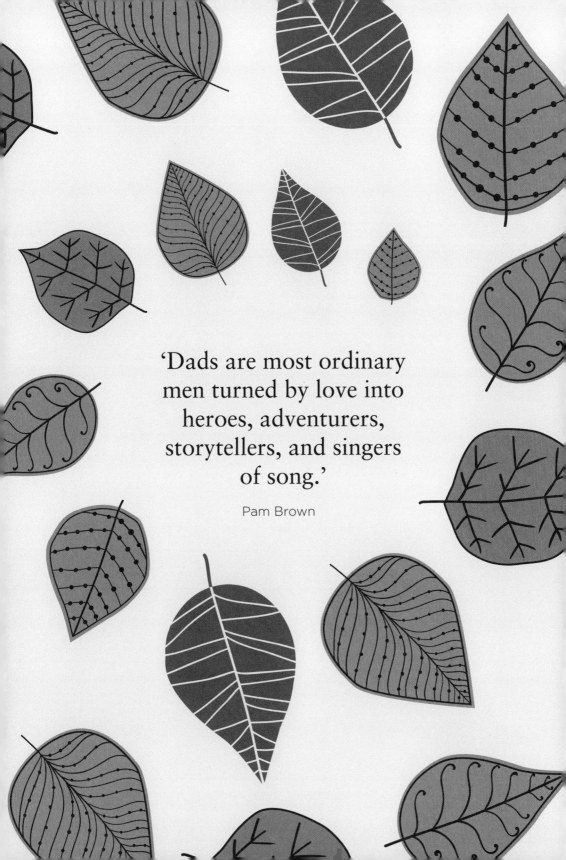

'Dads are most ordinary
men turned by love into
heroes, adventurers,
storytellers, and singers
of song.'

Pam Brown

Describe your wedding day, your celebration, or other significant events in your relationship.

....

....

....

....

....

....

....

....

....

....

....

....

What is your best memory of this time in your relationship?

....

....

....

....

....

....

....

....

....

....

....

....

....

....

....

Use this space to stick in photographs from significant moments in your relationship.

Did you always know you wanted children?

....
....
....
....
....

When did you find out you were going to become a parent?

....
....
....
....
....
....
....
....

Do you remember your thoughts when you first found out you were going to become a father?

....
....
....
....
....
....
....
....

What was the build-up to my arrival like?

....

....

....

....

....

....

....

....

....

....

....

....

....

....

....

....

....

....

....

....

....

....

Describe the day of my arrival. Where were you? Who were you with?

....
....
....
....
....
....
....
....
....
....
....
....
....
....
....
....
....
....
....
....
....

Describe your emotions on the day I arrived.
How did you feel when you first held me in your arms?

....
....
....
....
....
....
....
....
....
....
....
....
....
....
....
....
....
....
....
....
....
....

What events were happening in the world around the time I was born?

....
....
....
....
....
....
....
....
....
....
....
....
....
....
....
....
....
....
....
....
....
....
....

'My father gave
me the greatest gift
anyone could give
another person, he
believed in me.'

Jim Valvano

How did you choose my name?

....

....

....

....

....

....

....

Did you have any second choices? If so, what were they?

....

....

....

....

....

....

....

How did you choose my brother's/sister's names (if applicable)?

....

....

....

....

....

....

Describe the day-to-day routine at home during the first months of my life.

....

....

....

....

....

....

....

....

....

....

....

....

....

....

....

....

....

....

....

....

....

What songs or nursery rhymes did you sing to me?

....
....
....
....
....
....

What stories did you read to me?

....
....
....
....
....
....

What were my favourite songs or stories?

....
....
....
....
....
....
....

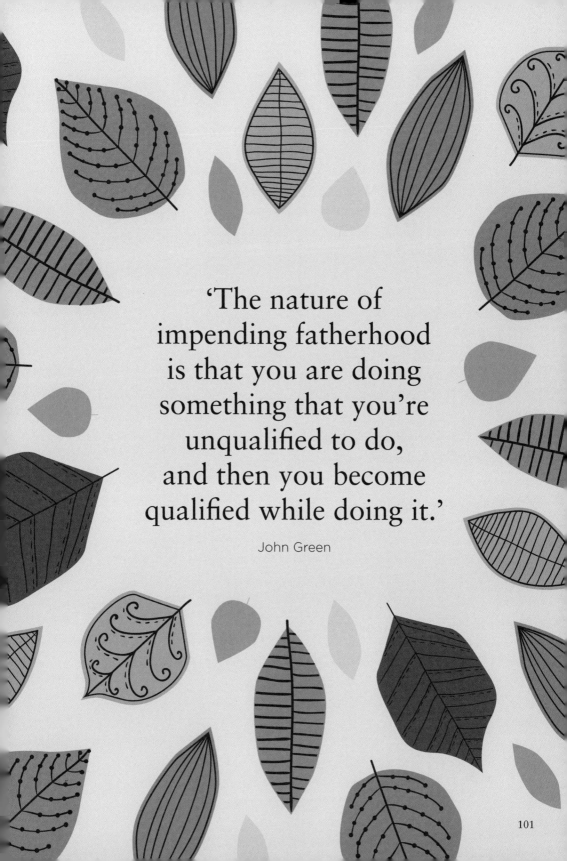

'The nature of
impending fatherhood
is that you are doing
something that you're
unqualified to do,
and then you become
qualified while doing it.'

John Green

What sort of child was I when I was very young?

....
....
....
....
....
....
....
....
....
....
....
....
....
....
....
....
....
....
....
....
....
....

In what ways am I most like you?

....

....

....

....

....

....

....

....

....

....

In what ways am I different to you?

....

....

....

....

....

....

....

....

....

....

Did you have strong ideas about how you wanted me to be brought up?

....

....

....

....

....

....

....

....

....

....

Did you stick to those ideas, or did they change?

....

....

....

....

....

....

....

....

....

....

....

....

In what ways did your life change when you became a father?

....
....
....
....
....
....
....
....

What was the most difficult aspect of fatherhood?

....
....
....
....
....
....
....
....
....
....
....

What games did you like to play with me?

....

....

....

....

....

....

What was the funniest thing I ever did when I was little?

....

....

....

....

....

....

....

What was the naughtiest or scariest thing I ever did?

....

....

....

....

....

....

If you have any photographs from when I was very young, stick them in here.

Write down all the 'family sayings' that you can remember – pet names, nicknames and other special phrases particular to our family.

....

....

....

....

....

....

....

....

....

....

....

....

....

....

....

....

....

....

....

....

....

Write a list of the meals or foods we ate,
or include a favourite recipe.

....

....

....

....

....

....

....

....

....

....

....

....

....

....

....

....

....

....

....

....

....

....

....

....

HOMES, HOLIDAYS AND TRAVEL

List all the addresses you've ever lived at.

....

....

....

....

....

....

....

....

....

....

....

....

....

....

....

....

....

....

....

....

....

....

....

Which was your favourite home, and why?

....
....
....
....
....
....
....
....
....
....
....
....
....
....
....
....
....
....
....
....
....
....
....
....
....

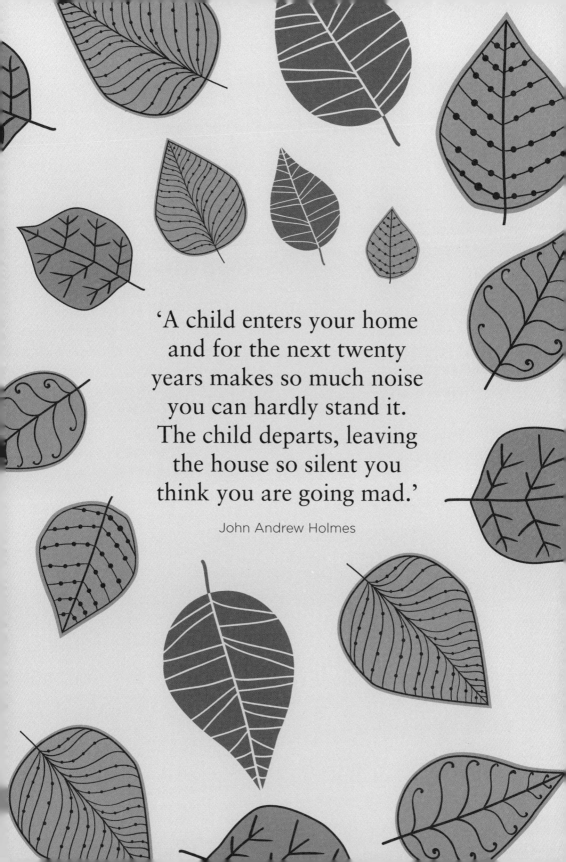

'A child enters your home
and for the next twenty
years makes so much noise
you can hardly stand it.
The child departs, leaving
the house so silent you
think you are going mad.'

John Andrew Holmes

Describe our family traditions during important holidays and celebrations.

··
··
··
··
··
··
··
··
··
··
··
··
··
··
··
··
··
··
··
··
··
··
··
··

Which family tradition do you cherish the most, and why?

List the locations of all the best holidays you've had.
Add the years if you can remember them.

....
....
....
....
....
....
....
....
....
....
....
....
....
....
....
....
....
....
....
....
....

Stick in some holiday photographs here.

PHILOSOPHY OF LIFE

Do you have any religious or spiritual beliefs?
If so, what are they?

....

....

....

....

....

....

....

....

....

....

....

....

....

....

....

....

....

....

....

....

....

....

....

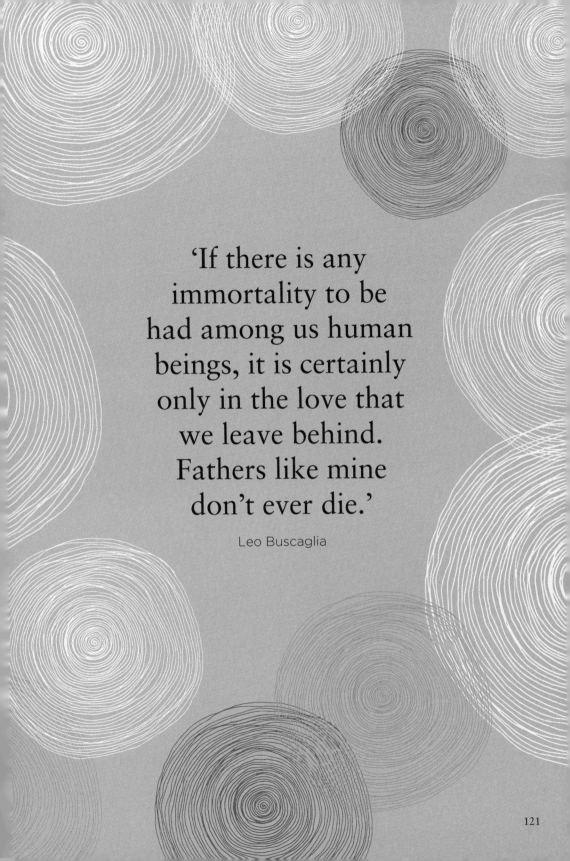

'If there is any
immortality to be
had among us human
beings, it is certainly
only in the love that
we leave behind.
Fathers like mine
don't ever die.'

Leo Buscaglia

What are your political beliefs?

....

....

....

....

....

....

....

....

....

....

....

....

....

....

....

....

....

....

....

....

....

....

Which politicians, leaders or famous people do you most respect and admire, and why?

....
....
....
....
....
....
....
....
....
....
....
....
....
....
....
....
....
....
....
....
....
....
....

What were the biggest decisions you ever made in your life?
For each decision, why did you choose that particular path?

....

....

....

....

....

....

....

....

....

....

....

....

....

....

....

....

....

....

....

....

....

What do you consider to be your greatest achievements?

....

....

....

....

....

....

....

....

....

....

Which one are you most proud of?

....

....

....

....

....

....

....

....

....

....

....

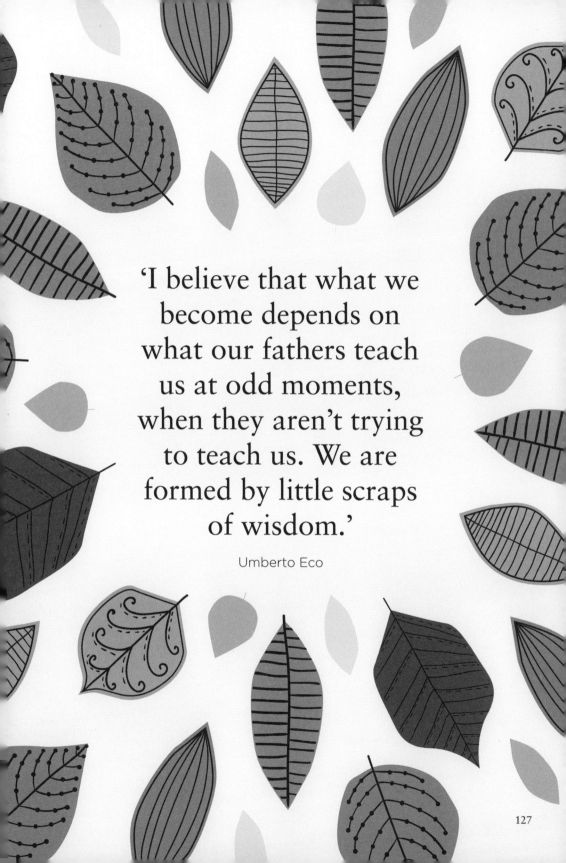

'I believe that what we become depends on what our fathers teach us at odd moments, when they aren't trying to teach us. We are formed by little scraps of wisdom.'

Umberto Eco

What is your biggest regret?

....

....

....

....

....

....

....

....

....

....

....

....

....

....

....

....

....

....

....

....

....

....

Is there anything in life you wish you'd made more time for?

....
....
....
....
....
....
....

Is there anything you wish you'd spent less time doing?

....
....
....
....
....
....
....

What would you do on your 'perfect day'?

....
....
....
....
....
....
....

What do you miss most about the 'good old days'?

....
....
....
....
....
....
....
....
....
....
....
....
....
....
....
....
....
....
....
....
....
....
....
....
....
....

What are your thoughts about the world today?

....
....
....
....
....
....
....
....
....
....
....
....
....
....
....
....
....
....
....
....
....
....
....
....

How does it feel getting older?

....

....

....

....

....

....

....

....

....

In what ways have you changed from the person you used
to be to the person you are now?

....

....

....

....

....

....

....

....

....

....

....

....

....

What advice would you give someone about to become a father for the first time?

....

....

....

....

....

....

....

....

....

....

....

....

....

....

....

....

....

....

....

....

....

....

If you were marooned on a desert island, what would you take with you, and why?

....
....
....
....
....
....
....
....
....
....
....
....
....
....
....
....
....
....
....
....
....
....
....
....
....

What is the best decision you ever made in your life?

....
....
....
....
....
....
....
....
....
....

If you had to do it all again, what would you do differently?

....
....
....
....
....
....
....
....
....
....
....

What happy memories will you treasure forever?

....
....
....
....
....
....
....
....
....
....
....

What are your saddest memories?

....
....
....
....
....
....
....
....
....
....
....
....
....

What makes you laugh the most?

What makes you feel afraid?

....
....
....
....
....
....
....
....
....
....

If you could go back in time, what advice would you give to
your younger self at age 20, 30 and 40?

....
....
....
....
....
....
....
....
....
....
....

....

....

....

....

....

....

....

....

....

....

....

If there was something in your life you could do again, what would it be?

....

....

....

....

....

....

....

....

....

....

....

....

....

Do you have interesting dreams? What happens in them, and what do you think they mean?

....

....

....

....

....

....

....

....

....

....

....

....

....

....

....

....

....

....

....

....

....

....

Is there anything you've always wanted to tell me, but haven't had the courage to?

....
....
....
....
....
....
....
....
....
....
....
....
....
....
....
....
....
....
....
....

Are there any questions you've ever wanted to ask me? Please list them here.

....

....

....

....

....

....

....

....

....

....

....

....

....

....

....

....

....

....

....

....

....

How would you like to be remembered?

....
....
....
....
....
....
....
....
....
....

What is your motto in life?

....
....
....
....
....
....
....
....
....
....
....

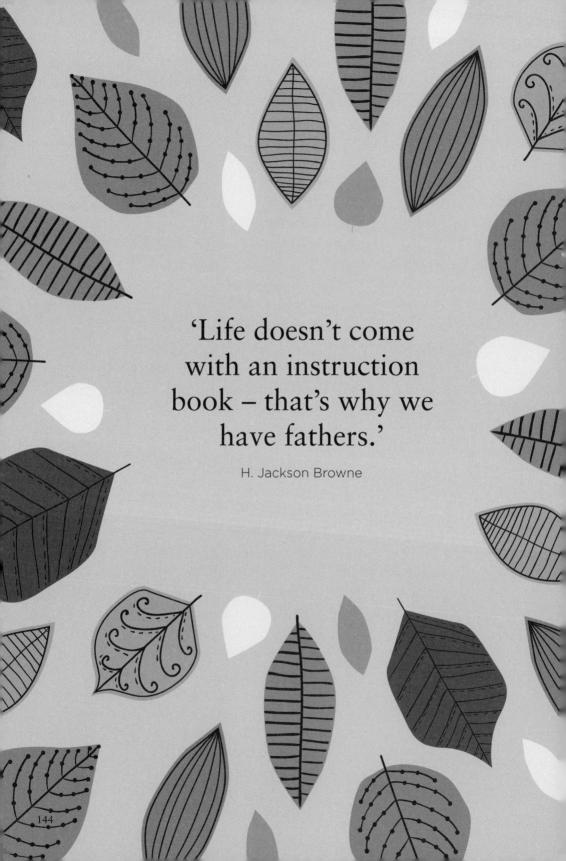

'Life doesn't come
with an instruction
book – that's why we
have fathers.'

H. Jackson Browne